*This book
belongs to...*

The Heath Fairies

Illustrated by

Margaret W. Tarrant

Original poetry by

Marion St. John Webb

Series Editor

Fiona Waters

· MARGARET TARRANT'S ·
FAIRIES & FLOWERS

First published in this format in 2003 by
The Medici Society Ltd
Grafton House, Hyde Estate Road, London NW9 6JZ

Copyright © The Medici Society Ltd 2003 / 1927

First published in 1927 by The Medici Society Ltd
1 3 5 7 9 10 8 6 4 2

A catalogue record for this book is available from the British Library.

ISBN 0 85503 251 0

Margaret Tarrant's original artworks have been rescanned for this re-designed edition.

Designed by Tony Potter Publishing Ltd

Printed in Singapore

The
Heath Fairies

Contents

And the Fairies didn't Know

Up on the heath the fairies danced,
    And I was there to see.
Nobody saw me watching them,
For I hid behind a tree.

Up on the heath the fairies sang,
And I was there to hear.
Nobody saw me listening,
To their songs so sweet and clear.

Up on the heath the fairies played,
Over the heather bright.
'We know everything!' they said,
But I knew that wasn't right.

Up on the heath the fairies laughed,
At how little mortals knew.
Fairies might be clever folk
But I was laughing too.

For not one fairy knew, you see,
That I was there, behind the tree!

Come to the Fair

Ding, dong! Ding, dong!
　　　　Are you coming to the fair?
There are fairy rings and fairy swings
And all kinds of magic things.
Oh, say you'll come, I'll see you there!

Ding, dong! Ding, dong!
All the fairies will be there.
The Fairy Queen you're bound to see
As she sips her cowslip tea.
Oh, please do come, if you dare!

Ding, dong! Ding, dong!
The fairy cooks have done their share.
There'll be plates of cakes so sweet
That you would simply love to eat.
So, please do come, and see the fairy fair!

Nothing so Nice

"There's nothing so nice as a
    little fat fly,
Excepting perhaps a little fat fairy.
A fly makes the tastiest dinner, say I,
But perhaps my diet I should vary."

So chuckled the sundew, a cunning
  heath-plant,
Who caught and would eat the flies
  that flew by him.
"He shan't catch little fat fairies –
  he shan't!"
The fairies cried, and their faces
  were grim.

A fairy by day and a glow-worm by
  night
Stood guard by the sundew, just as a
  warning
To all the fat fairies and heath-flies
  who might
Come by late at night or early in the
  morning.

It's no use the sundew plant
  whining,
"You'll starve me! Each day I grow
  thinner!"
For everyone says it is perfectly fair,
He has plenty good things for his
  dinner!

But like many people, whom I'm
   sure you have met
The things he wants most are the
   things he can't get!

The Three Policemen

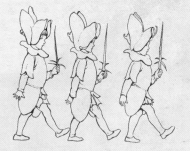

Beside the bush of golden gorse
    There was a sunny little dell,
Many children came to play there,
And sometimes to picnic as well.

But often they were very careless.
They trampled in and trampled out,
And left a lot of bits and scraps,
And paper bags lying about.

The fairies on the heath were vexed
At all these nasty, messy things.
"We'll have to put a stop to this,"
They said and crossly shook their wings.

They had a meeting, and they talked
From one o'clock till half past eight.
And then they sent three fairies off
To hide inside the bush and wait.

The Three Policemen they were called
By every fairy, one and all.
And from the gorse the three plucked
   thorns
And straight like swords, they held
   them tall.

"Now when the naughty children come
And scatter paper bags and bread,
We'll use these thorns, and make them
   run!"
The Three Policemen said.

Beneath the bush of golden gorse
They stood and waited all the day.
But no one came inside the dell
Not to picnic, nor to play.

And all the next day and the next,
The Three Policemen waited there.
But still the children did not come
The fairies started to despair.

"Now can it be that someone's told
The children that we're hiding here?"
The Three Policemen asked, then
   sighed,
"Is that why they don't come near?"

But no one knew, and so at length
The Three Policemen slipped away
For just a short while, to eat and sleep
And then to have a little play.

They left the dell all clean and tidy,
And everything was neat and right,
But when they came on guard again,
They saw a shocking sight!

Once more the children had been there!
They'd trampled in and trampled out,
Throwing scraps and paper bags,
They'd left a lot of things about!

Somebody Listens

What do fairies talk about
        When they're out to tea?
Do they talk of fairy magic,
Or things like you and me?

Somebody saw two fairies once
Sitting in a tree,
Eating kernels from a cone,
As cheerful as could be.

Somebody thought, "Ah, now at last
I'll hear some fairy things."
Somebody waited . . . and then
One fairy stretched his wings,
Rubbed his hands, and rubbed his knees,
Then he said, "More fir-cones, please."

Paying the Rent

A sad little fairy walked under
   the bracken,
It was all withered and old,
For it was autumn, and the frost came
   to blacken,
And the winds blew so very cold.
She sighed for her house, beaten down
   by the weather,
Her house made of bracken and moss.
Then making a fire with some twigs
   and old heather,
She sat down to think of her loss.

And while she sat thinking, a wee
   mouse came creeping,
And watched her with big, wistful eyes.

"I wonder . . . I wonder . . . ," the mouse
   thought, still peeping.
"Oh, shall I speak — will it be wise?"

And then the mouse saw the fairy
  was crying!
"Dear fairy, don't cry," said the mouse.
"I'm looking for someone to come as
  a lodger,
And live with me in my warm little
  house."

"The parlour is snug, and the
    bedroom is airy.
I've put up a notice to say,
'Apartments to let, for a mouse or a
    fairy.'
Perhaps you should come right away?"

"Dear mouse," said the fairy, "do lead
    the way!
But what is the rent, if you please?"
The mouse said, "For bed and
    breakfast each day,
My charge is a strong bit of cheese."

And so, when some folks are
 sleeping,
Their mouse-traps are emptied and
 bent,
For the fairy flies down, and silently
 creeping,
Takes out the cheese, for her rent!

Margaret Winifred Tarrant (1888 - 1959)

'Every time a child says, " I don't believe in fairies," ' warned Peter Pan, 'there is a little fairy somewhere that falls down dead.' By her paintings Margaret Tarrant did as much to encourage children's belief in fairies as J M Barrie did by his writings. Born in London in 1888, the only child of artist Percy Tarrant and his wife Sarah, Margaret excelled at art from an early age, and she was only 19 when she received her first, very prestigious, commission, from J M Dent & Sons: to illustrate Charles Kingsley's much-loved children's classic, *The Water Babies*, which was first published in 1863.

Her delicate, charming pictures matched the spirit of the story perfectly and earned her a string of new commissions: *Nursery Rhymes* (1914 and 1923), *Alice in Wonderland* (1916) and

Hans Andersen's Fairy Tales (1917) for Ward Lock & Co., plus postcards for Oxford University Press.

Margaret Tarrant illustrated some 20 books for George G. Harrap & Co. between 1915 and 1929, but an even more important publishing relationship began in 1920, when she completed her first pieces for The Medici Society. This was to prove a long and fruitful connection, resulting in most of her best-known work. In the 1920s, for example, she illustrated this highly successful series of fairy books for the company, written by the poet and author Marion St John Webb. Her picture of Peter's Friends, inspired by J M Barrie's *Peter Pan* stories and the statue in Kensington Gardens, proved so popular when it appeared in 1921 that it had to be reproduced many times.

Peter's Friends

The dusk of the nineteenth and dawn of the twentieth centuries were magical times for fairy lovers. Fascination with fairy lore was widespread, reaching unprecedented heights in 1922 when Sir Arthur Conan Doyle published *The Coming of the Fairies*, containing 'photographs' of fairies taken by two young girls in a Yorkshire village, which were later proved to be hoaxes. The story was actually a fascinating deception, which was believed by many reputable people. The mystery was not solved until towards the end of the twentieth century, when the girls involved, now elderly ladies, explained what had really happened.

In 1922, Margaret Tarrant's *Do You Believe in Fairies?* showed two children encircled by a ring of fairies, which caught the public excitement already created by Sir Arthur Conan Doyle's book.

This interest was mirrored in an outpouring of art and literature. Children's books cultivated belief in fairies: they were used in religious teaching, magazines were devoted to them, and captivating new works appeared, most notably J M Barrie's *Peter Pan* and *Peter Pan in Kensington Gardens*. Rudyard Kipling wrote *Rewards and Fairies* and even Beatrix Potter embraced the subject in *The Fairy Caravan*.

Artists revelled in the opportunity to portray imaginary worlds. Arthur Rackham, the most fashionable illustrator of his day, depicted a sinister fantasy landscape, peopled by spiky goblins, fairies and mice amid gnarled trees with gnomelike faces. In contrast, Honor Appleton, Maud Tindal Atkinson and Mabel Lucie Atwell offered gentler, comforting images recalling Kate Greenaway's illustrations of apple-cheeked children.

Margaret Tarrant was one of those most associated with the depiction of fairies in the 1920s and 1930s, together with her friend and sketching partner, Cicely Mary Barker (1895 - 1973). Both began to use Art Nouveau and Arts and Crafts

elements in their work, and in Tarrant's paintings a breathtaking attention to detail - diaphanous wings with the intricate tracery of a dragonfly's wings - is a testament to the reality of fairies, imaginary or otherwise.

During her life Margaret Tarrant tackled a wide range of subjects and won special acclaim for those, such as *All Things Wise and Wonderful*, with a religious theme. But her forte was fairies, for in her evocation of these ethereal figures she could express her love for children, wild flowers and dance, of all that was beautiful and pure.

She would sketch meticulously from life to capture the likeness of a child or plant, then compose her pictures by arranging the subjects in imaginary settings, infusing them with a distinctive otherworldly quality.

Margaret Tarrant's fairies have a unique fluidity and balletic grace that expressed her delight in the free-flowing dance invented by Isadora Duncan. She was very much a free spirit herself, flying along the country lanes around her home in Surrey on an ancient bicycle, leaping off impulsively to sketch a flower or help a toddler to paint. She never married, but she attracted many friends by her generosity, energy and zest for life. Perhaps it was this childlike enthusiasm and innocence, combined with a special kind of imagination, that gave her a natural affinity with fairies.

The Lily Pool

Much missed when she died in 1959, Margaret Tarrant left a lasting legacy in charming pictures that seem as fresh today as the day they were painted, and still enchant new generations with their glimpses into a secret fairy world.

The new edition

There are 12 beautiful fairy books by Margaret Tarrant, originally published between 1923 - 1928. The re-designed edition is now available to collect as a set, with modern scanning methods used to bring out the exquisite detail of the original paintings and drawings.

WATER FAIRIES

WATER FAIRIES

TWILIGHT FAIRIES

TWILIGHT FAIRIES

WEATHER FAIRIES

WEATHER FAIRIES

ORCHARD FAIRIES

ORCHARD FAIRIES

WILD FRUIT FAIRIES

FRUIT FAIRIES

INSECT FAIRIES

INSECT FAIRIES

HOUSE FAIRIES

HOUSE FAIRIES

FOREST FAIRIES

FOREST FAIRIES

SEED FAIRIES

SEED FAIRIES

SEASHORE FAIRIES

FLOWER FAIRIES

FLOWER FAIRIES

HEATH FAIRIES

HEATH FAIRIES

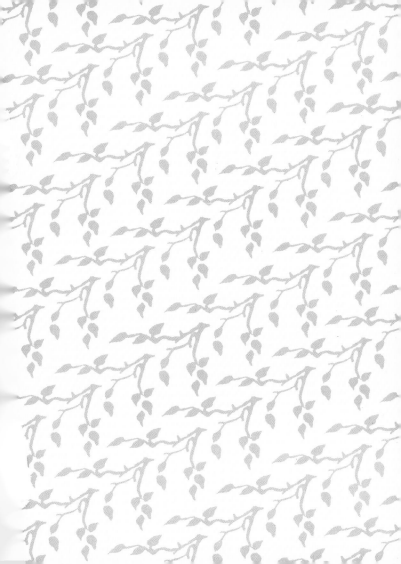